THE SHILDAM HALL TAPES

Design: Stephen Prince /A Year In The Country
The layout is based in part on design work by Ian Lowey of Bopcap Book Services, Manchester.

Other books by Stephen Prince:
A Year In The Country: Wandering Through Spectral Fields
A Year In The Country: Straying From The Pathways
A Year In The Country: The Marks Upon The Land
The Corn Mother

Albums by Stephen Prince:
The Corn Mother: Night Wraiths
The Shildam Hall Tapes: The Falling Reverse

Albums by Stephen Prince (working as A Year In The Country):
Airwaves: Songs From The Sentinels
No More Unto The Dance
Undercurrents

THE SHILDAM HALL TAPES

Stephen Prince

1/4

1799: Sarah

We knew it could never be. It was not merely our differences: me a lady from the Hall and him a travelling labourer. It was also him being a wanderer and the call for him to set off once again would arrive when the summer was out.

I had taken to wandering the moors alone, it clears the head and is a balm for my aching heart. It is not allowed or approved of, but I say that I am going to read in the library – it is rarely used so I shall not be missed – and then quietly make my way out here.

One day, when I was walking these harsh but beautiful fen-lands, it came to me, like a whisper on the wind: a song fully formed as though it were a siren song from an old soul.

I rushed home and transcribed it, my hand shaking as I did so. But none shall ever hear it, not even my love. It shall be my own private lullaby for my gentle Johnny.

1840: Helena

I was terribly bored this morning. There is really not a lot to do here out of season. Yes, the Hall is terribly grand and the envy of all other great houses in the county, but really, what is a girl to do with herself during the darkest months of the winter?

And that is how I found myself wandering around the library.

I hardly ever go there. All the books are terribly serious: academic tomes, theology and the like. Do not tell mama as she would very much disapprove, but I prefer a good romance or even a penny dreadful or two. One of the maids, Alice, used to sneak them to me. They are terribly thrilling. Quite frightful really but I do seem to enjoy them so.

The pity of it is that I have not read one for a while as Alice upped and got married and she and her new beau have moved to the city. I have heard they have jobs in a mill.

Tucked away in the corner of a high shelf I found a smallish box. It was quite ornate and rather lovely. I had never noticed it before but I took it down to investigate further.

Inside were some papers and a journal: really nothing all that much of interest, except that at the back of the journal was a sheet of handwritten music. For once I was glad that mama had insisted that I keep up my music lessons, and I do not know what possessed me, but I began to sing the song.

1840: Alice

I heard all about Miss Helena. She took a tumble in the Hall's library. She didn't fall far – just off that little ladder they have in there – but she fell awkwardly: came down with more than a bump. It is said that she ails, and she'll be recovering for a fair while.

1908: Marie

It is the most marvellous thing. Papa bought it, although he says he wishes he hadn't: our very own cylinder phonograph. And what fun I have had with it, recording myself singing and reciting poems.

Papa grumbles about the cost of the cylinders but he does not truly care. It is hardly as though they are going to bankrupt the family.

Great grandpapa does not share my love of the phonograph: far from it. He says that soon we will be able to hear the voices of dead men through it, and that only God is meant to hear the voices of those who are gone.

Still, I think it is jolly good fun being able to record one's singing and then listen to it whenever one likes.

It is in the library at the moment, which of course is something else for papa to grumble about. Apparently, the library is meant to be a place for thinking and study, not "novelty and noise from those infernal spinning tubes".

He is away today – something to do with Farbrook farms and the new tenants – so I have the library and the wonderful new contraption all to myself.

Hmmm, now what is this? I have not seen that before. It is a rather lovely box. I think I shall investigate further.

1908: Ada

If I've warned young Cedric once, I've warned him a hundred times that he is to stay out of the library unless he is asked in to carry out his duties. But he's drawn to the place. I think at heart he wishes he could go off to university, as the young master of the house has done, and the library is the nearest he is ever likely to get to such a place.

And it's not just the books of late. He's fascinated by that new-fangled cylinder phonograph that Miss Marie is always using. I said to leave well alone, but he didn't listen.

He was found in a faint on the library floor. It's them old gas-light fittings in there: I've said before that there was something not right about them. One was leaking and the gas overcame him.

It's been such a worry but the doctor said he will be fine. He will merely need a few days rest and plenty of good country air.

It was obvious to all that he'd been using the cylinder pho-nograph. They found a recording Miss Marie made next to it. There'll be heck to pay about that: Cedric'll be in for a roasting when he returns.

I half-heard the Mistress of the house giving Miss Marie a dressing down, though I couldn't quite hear what was being said.

When I saw Miss Marie later that day she looked most cha-grined and down in her spirits.

1908: Augusta

I have told Marie that she will no longer be wasting her time with such fripperies and flights of fancy as recording her singing on that machine. I said in no uncertain terms that from now she is only to concentrate on preparations for her introduction to society, and that all her cylinder recordings will be put away.

2/4

1969: Dave

Things have been going great with the band. I think we're close to signing a deal with this record company that's been interested for a while. Their A&R guy who "discovered" us when we were playing a residency in a little basement club in Soho is a young guy, knows what he's on about, seems to get where we're coming from. Which makes a change from some of the plums in suits we've talked to before.

And now we've got this gig lined up out in the countryside. We've been asked to do the soundtrack for a film. I don't know all that much about it, but they seem to be throwing money about. You wouldn't believe how much we're getting paid.

We could just record in a studio but apparently the director wants us on location: something about immersing ourselves in the creative process of making the film.

1969: Peter

I've been writing for this underground magazine for a while now. It's a good gig: quite a laugh actually. I've been writing about the hippie and psychedelic culture that's all the rage at the mo'. A lot of the time it means being stuck listening to some godawful free-form poetry at some happening or other but this, well, this is different.

I'm on location, reporting on this film that's being made in some country pile. All kinds of money seems to be involved: proper Hollywood-style money. It's not just some little experimental thing.

And this place is grand I tell y'. The booze (and other things) is flowing freely, there's right posh grub, a lovely four-poster bed to sleep in. It all makes a change from my bedsit in Notting Hill. Not that I don't love it there, right in the heart of things, but it's nice to eat something proper for a change: something that hasn't fallen out of a can or that isn't swilled up at my local greasy caff.

The place is owned by this young toff called Joshua. I know him from around town: I've seen him at some of the more "out there" events. He's swallowed the whole "new psychedelic world" idea hook line and sinker. It's quite sweet really. I don't want to sound too cynical – I can appreciate what people are trying to do, where they're coming from – but I'd rather try and be a bit more objective about it all.

Still, it's probably easier to be a star child when your old man's left you somewhere like this, and what's said to be more money than you could easily spend in a lifetime. I expect it's a bit easier to look to a bright new future when you're not having to scrabble around in your sock drawer for a few bob you might have overlooked to feed the meter.

1969: Joshua

Father would have never understood all this. He loved tradition, respectability, things being just so and staying that way forever.

But there's a whole new world out there: a whole new way of living just there for the taking. And I'm taking it: I'm taking it all.

Talking of which, maybe I was taking it all just a little too much last night. And the night before and, well, to be honest for quite a while now. I'm still a bit fuzzy round the edges. More than a little really. I seem to be that way a lot of late.

But it's all part and parcel of this bright new vision of the world and how it shall come into being: all part of the great experiment.

So, mustn't grumble. Chin up. The film crew's here and it's going to be a glorious month or two.

1969: Peter

I'll tell you what: this band they've got in are the business. They're really tight heavy psych rock. And from what I've heard they've been brewing up some great tunes. I reckon these boys will go far.

1969: Fred

I met this young lad in a club in Soho that we've got an interest in. He was alright, one of them hippie psychedelic types. A bit daft maybe but just young and idealistic really. Let's face it, we all were once.

What he also was, was titled gentry. He had very deep pockets and didn't mind reaching into them for "the cause". That often seemed to just mean bankrolling half the club's drinking habits and then letting a load of freeloaders come back to your pad in Kensington and start work on your old man's wine collection.

His title came with something else besides the cash: a prime old plot out in the country. Lovely gaff. Grand I think you'd say. And that's just what we were looking for.

So I give him the chat, in a roundabout way. Well, what I actually did was got Janet to talk to him about the film as I thought he'd respond better to somebody nearer his own age than he would to me.

The thing is with Janet, she might dress like one of those hippies but she's as sharp as a tack: sharper, if anything. She knew exactly what he wanted to hear: told him how the film was going to push back boundaries, to be the first legitimate and truthful expression of the psychedelic dream.

And it might just be true. Even somebody who's been around the block a few times like me, seen a fair few of these youthful crazes and the passions they briefly ignite, can tell that the director isn't just some fly-by-night hoping to cash in on it all. He's got what I think you could call a vision.

1969: Janet

We got it all set up with Joshua so that we could film at Shildam Hall. He's just glad to be involved really: glad to be part of it all.

And me? I'm hoping for a producer's credit on the film. Or at the very least assistant producer. If things turn out right this is going to be my ticket up and out of here, across the pond to Hollywood I'm thinking. We'll have to see: see how it all goes.

1969: Penelope

It's not a bad job this one. I've worked on film costume before but nothing on this scale: there's no expense spared. They gave me some outlines of what they wanted but they're giving me plenty of creative freedom about what I do. I'm thinking of a cross between dandy, highwayman and psychedelic club peacock, if that makes sense, for the male lead. I'm not sure yet about the female lead: whether to go more cosmic and ethereal or something a bit more vampishly rogueish. It's difficult to properly get a bead on what to do, as the script seems to be changing daily.

1969: Jeff

I've been taking myself off from the rest of the band and working on something else, something less rock orientated. I've kept it to myself and not told anybody in the band: not played them anything. I'm just enjoying working on it on my own. I've set up a bit of recording equipment over in the East Wing, away from everybody else.

I've been listening to some of that folk rock that's started to get popular. I think it's interesting how it's reinterpreted traditional folk, but I thought you could push it further: take it somewhere else.

That was part of what inspired me, but really what set me off was this old wax-recording cylinder that I found in a box in the library. And surprisingly, sitting in a corner, was one of the machines for playing it on. I don't know why but I fancied a listen to the cylinder, and with a bit of trial and error, and coaxing, I managed to get the machine working.

This beautiful voice tumbled out of the machine's horn. It seemed to linger and float around the room. It was a woman singing an old folk song and it just rooted me to the spot. I think I must have just stood there for ten minutes after it had finished, completely lost, somewhere else.

Try as I might I couldn't get the machine to play the cylinder again and I could barely remember the song – more its spirit or atmosphere rather than the specifics of it – but it seemed to spark something in me.

Since then I've quietly worked on my ideas, honing the music and pressing it into shape, subtly mixing elements of psychedelia in with a folkish sound.

I particularly like the song that was inspired by that recording on the wax cylinder. I've done a few versions of that. They've got a sparkle or glow unlike anything I've heard before. They're both new, but also seem as though they have been around forever.

1969: Paul

The film crew needed some time to set up lights in a new location and they didn't need us extras for a while so after I'd eaten I was wandering around some part of the Hall I'd not been in before. It was off over in the East Wing, while we're set up in the West side. Apparently, this side of the Hall isn't really used anymore

It was then that I heard it: this music, off in the distance. It was like something I'd known all my life but I'm sure I'd not heard it before.

I couldn't tell where it was coming from, but I stood transfixed. I don't know how long I was there for.

After that I wandered around a bit, exploring, trying to find where the music had come from but there are so many rooms and corridors in this place and some of the doors look the same as the panelling, so it's not always obvious where you can go in or through.

Eventually I had to give up and wandered back to the others, to see what was going on.

1970: Peter

Remember I said I was doing a report from a film location? Well, the first one went down well and so I'm back for a follow-up piece.

And...

I've been here for weeks now. Well I think I have: I'm not sure any more. This place has become like a bubble that once you step into you can't get out of. It wasn't like that before, it was just a regular film set. Yeh, people were partying a bit afterhours but nothing too heavy.

But this. Now. This is too heavy.

1970: Joshua

We must press on. We must press further. Out into the stars. The cosmos. It is our mission and our duty.

This is no longer merely a film. This is a reflection, a channelling of a new world. It is a brave, brave new world. And it is one entirely of our creation.

1970: Elsie

I've worked here all my life: I'm downstairs staff. I help keep it all running smoothly, make sure the fires are stoked, the silver's polished, the moths and mice are kept at bay...

But that young Joshua: I knew no good would come of him inheriting the title so young. Now his dad, he was a proper gentleman. He could be a bit stiff and formal but he had his head on his shoulders.

But Joshua's head: well, that's just been turned. More like spun round so fast that it's never stopping. I've heard them, up all night, partying.

Now don't get me wrong, I like a good knees-up myself, but not every night. And it has been every night. For weeks, maybe months now. It won't end well: it can't.

It started after that crowd of young folk turned up to be extras in the film they're making. Some of them never left again: they're camped out in the West Wing. It's like one of them hippie communes that I've read about in the papers.

I understand wanting to be footloose and fancy free when you're young. I never got the chance to do it myself – too sensible – but sometimes I wonder what it would've been like... What a different life might have been like.

But there's different and there's different. And I'm not sure I understand all this.

And what have they done in the old library? All those marks on the floor, the candles burnt down and dripping everywhere. Some kind of incense or something lingering in the air.

1970: Fred

I don't know what happened. When I last came down here things all seemed cushty. The director seemed right on it, and the dailies looked great.

And then I had to go away for a week or few: some problems back on the manor. Something that needed sorting, cleaning up and then when I got back, it was like this... This mess. Most of the budget's gone and so's half the film that's been shot. Nobody seems to know where it is.

And now the director's saying that he's quitting, that he can't work like this, not with everybody in this kind of state. Not that he looks like he's been living a squeaky clean life out here mind.

James really isn't going to be happy about this: not happy at all. And I'm in the firing line. It was me that suggested we branch out a bit from all the tried and tested money earners that we had. I thought it might be a way of going a bit more legitimate. A way of flushing all that cash clean.

It was branching out more than a bit really and I might've bitten off more than I can chew.

1970: Dave

I'm not sure how much more I can stand of all this. This isn't what I signed up for.

I think we were supposed to just be here for a few weeks: put down some tracks and then leave. I can't quite remember. Jeff dealt with all the paperwork.

And the music. Now I'm quite open minded about different styles and recording techniques. I'll listen to what's new, but this?

I'll tell you a secret. The band's actually been together for a few years. We're not old codgers but not quite spring chickens either. We've tried a few different things, a few different names and styles. We'd been part of the blues boom, gone a bit mod and then we'd started to add psychedelic touches to the music. But we always kept a core of melody, of accessibility. Our sound had developed nicely into a heavy psych rock sound.

But then we got here and it all went to pot. Literally I guess. It wasn't Jeff so much as some of the others in the band. There was a power struggle. Jeff fought for a while but he seemed distracted and after a while he just gave up. And then it was all tape loops, theremins, Mellotrons and somebody got hold of one of those Moog synthesizers. Lord knows how, as they cost an absolute packet.

There was a lot of addled talk about the tyranny of traditional musical forms and the tunes, the melodies: they just disappeared off into the ether.

1970: Peter

Owww, my head. I got drawn into it all. I've only got so much willpower and when it's all there on a plate I was always going to buckle.

I'm not quite sure what happened yesterday. I was typing up some notes when I heard them all starting downstairs. It wasn't even noon yet. I thought I'd pop down there and see what was going on.

And that was that really. It all started to get a bit licentious in more ways than one and I was just reeling by mid-afternoon. I sort of half-remember wandering down into the village with somebody from the production company. She was called Jane or Janet I think. I have a vague memory of her sitting me down in a cafe for a while, trying to get me to eat something, have a cup of tea: trying to bring me back down to earth.

And now there's something just niggling away at the edge of my memory from yesterday. Something about a junkshop maybe? Loads of old bric-a-brac. I seem to remember sitting down while she looked around. There were these old journals I was flipping through, I think. Something about life in a village and a Ms Jessworth was it? I don't know...

All I really know now is that I need to get out of here.

1970: *The Shildam Weekly Reporter*

An ambulance was called to Shildam Hall on Wednesday after an accident in a pond involving a Paul Harford who was working as an extra in a film which is being made on location at the Hall.

Further details of the incident are not known but the patient is said to be making a full recovery in hospital.

1970: Jeff

At the end of being at Shildam I had a huge row with the others in the band. It started as my last ditch attempt to bring everybody back together: to try and knock some kind of sense into us all. And it just degenerated. It was ugly. Things were said… Things you can't unsay. I'd had enough and I left. Just before what happened in one of the ponds. That was a close call.

I managed to get a lift back into town with this bloke called Fred, and Janet somebody. They were part of the production company. He seemed like a bit of a heavy, not in as good shape as he might once have been but looked like he could still handle himself. Like you still wouldn't want to cross him. They had this other lass with them: her name was Jenny or Jenine maybe. She didn't say much: seemed a bit spaced out.

I'd pretty much finished the music I'd been working on separately to the band but it wasn't until I got home that I realised I didn't have the final edit tapes with me or their duplicates. I thought I'd picked them up. I was sure I had but I mustn't have done.

I couldn't face going back to get them. It was all too fresh and raw. I just wanted to forget about it all.

And then once the dust had settled, I tried to get in touch with somebody at the Hall but it was closed down. I'm not sure what had happened but the Hall itself was up for sale and all the contents had been sold off in a rush. I tried to track down where they'd gone to, who'd bought what but that just led nowhere.

I think it's time for a fresh start, somewhere new, time to leave the music scene behind.

1970: Fred

I don't like to play the heavy unless I have to, I'm trying to get away from all that but sometimes needs still must. Me and a few of the others headed down to the Fleet Street boozers, where all the journalists drink, and put the word about. Nothing was to be written about the goings on at Shildam Hall.

I'd heard that somebody from the papers had been asking around. And this story's got it all, everything they love to write about: hippies and degenerate youth out of control, drugs, excess. Mix that in with some aristo type who's been drawn into that world, me and the fellas' connection and now this accident with the boy in the pond. If they start in on it there'll be a feeding frenzy.

So we put it about that the story is to be spiked, buried, forgotten about. And if it wasn't there'd be some words had and things could get properly uncomfortable.

I had to do it. If I hadn't the spotlight might have gone on where some of the money had come from for the film and we couldn't have that.

It was James as well. I've seen what he's like when he's backed into a corner, when he thinks the game's up. I've seen what's likely to happen then and it's not pretty. Not pretty at all.

1971: Joshua

It's all gone. Well, nearly all of it. I still have just enough to provide for myself.

It was that film. They put in some of the investment but behind the scenes it was mostly being made with my money. And it was an awful lot. It was almost everything. People think the family still had a great fortune but it was nothing like it once was.

I thought I was working towards some great bright future: that it was part of the great experiment. But it just all dissolved, like it did for a lot of us. Turned inwards, curdled, corrupted.

And then there was what happened in the lily pond. It was all very nearly a scandal but thankfully the nationals didn't pick up on the story, so the family name was saved at least. Father would have been thankful for that, if not much else.

And now here I am, living in this flat. One of the last remaining corners of the estate after the family home, centuries of history, like my generation's dreams, have all just blown away like dust.

1971: Joshua

It's time for a reassessment. Time to change. Rather than changing the world perhaps we should look to ourselves, to how we can expand our own consciousness.

I've been visiting this bookshop called Watkins just off Charing Cross Road in central London. It's a bit of a trek from my flat but worth it.

Any money I have spare, which is not much these days, I spend in there.

They have the most wonderful selection of books to help one explore one's own inner being. Spirituality, mysticism, esoteric beliefs. They can all be found there.

It really is something of a "University of Rejected Sciences".

1975: Dave

The band crumbled after all that mess at Shildam Hall. We were so close, right on the very edge of making it. Maybe. And then the drink and drugs took over. The endless arguing, people pulling in different directions. It was like being in three different bands at once.

When we first started recording the soundtrack we put down some blinding tracks before it all went off the rails. They weren't far off completed and you know what? I don't think they were just part of a soundtrack, I think it may well have been our first proper album.

If I'm honest it wasn't just the others who'd been indulging. I had as well by the end. Maybe not as much as some and that crew of hangers on who turned up to be extras and never left, but I certainly wasn't a bystander. That didn't help the situation. It didn't help me to stop and think for a moment about the practicalities when I was leaving. I just threw a few bits in a bag and was gone.

I don't know what happened to the tapes. At the end there I just wanted to leave as fast as I could. Especially after what happened with that lad Paul. It was a harbinger of worse to come I thought, if things weren't stopped.

And I don't know what happened to Jeff either. Nobody seemed to know. He seemed to just drop off the radar.

I've tried working with a few other people since then but nothing ever came of it. It's maybe time to think about hanging up my boots and getting a real job.

Whatever one of them is.

1976: Joshua

I was in Watkins recently talking to one of my fellow travellers in the inner sciences and he thrust a copy of a book into my hands. It's an anthology of television drama scripts by some chap called Nigel Kneale. I have to say I was more than a little sceptical about it. There's so much drivel on television, so little that's truly nourishing, although I do find some of *Leap in the Dark* and its exploring of the supernatural and paranormal quite intriguing.

One has to be careful though what one imbibes culturally, as the esoteric has gained a curious sensationalist populist appeal in recent years and that has lead to something of a flood of exploitational material.

My friend insisted that I read *The Stone Tape* in the anthology. He said that I might find it illuminating. His other recommendations have generally been somewhat excellent, so I may well put aside some time to read it.

While I was waiting to pay for my other purchases I noticed a book that another customer was buying. It was called *A Book of Dreams* and had the most intriguing surreal cover.

Dreams are a topic that I have a great interest in. I think they may at times be when our consciousness reaches beyond the Earthly veil, and so I asked this other customer about the book. She said it had just caught her eye, and she showed me the text on the back cover which described it as being some form of biography by the son of somebody who was persecuted for his work when trying to create his vision of the world as a place where dreams and reality were virtually indistinguishable.

Suddenly she looked at her watch and said she had to rush as she needed to be at a dance class nearby that started at two o'clock and with that she paid for her book and set off.

The Book of Dreams' topic wasn't quite what I expected from its title but it may be one to add to my list of future purchases as this chap's father's aims sound as though they may not be all that divergent from my own.

1976: Joshua

Well I must say, *The Stone Tape* was indeed intriguing and inspiring. Although it may have veered at points a little too much towards the strictures of Western empirical science, it also rather marvellously blended that with a tale of spirits from another realm and time.

In it, a team of modern electronic researchers decamp to an old mansion in order to develop a new form of recording medium. But rather than inventing yet another modern gizmo they accidentally unearth what appears to be not so much a ghostly haunting but a preserving of some kind of terrible incident that has come to be recorded in the stone of a room.

The story's location put me in mind of Shildam Hall.

Imagine if, as in *The Stone Tape*, I could have found some kind of ancient spirit or force recorded in the matter and material of the Hall.

1976: Joshua

The ideas in *The Stone Tape* seem to have taken hold of my imagination somewhat.

I've always considered that the events at Shildam Hall during the filming were merely the result of youthful excess, bad luck and poor management.

But what if it was something else? Something unexplained? I know that my memory of then is a little fogged by time and my own self-administered haze during that period but looking back it was as though there was something unearthly or preternatural at play. It seemed almost as if we had unearthed and suffered the wrath of a power beyond our ken.

I think it is worthy of investigation.

1976: Jenine

After coming back from Shildam Hall I just wanted a quiet life. I needed one really. My head was... fragmented. Fractured.

I was one of the flower children, with a head full of dreams and stardust and I was out nearly every night of the week.

One time at a club this woman called Janet turned up and she invited us to be extras in some film that was being made at a mansion in the country.

At the time I was footloose and fancy free and so I just went along with everybody else. There was a convoy of us in cars, vans, an old bus, all with Janet and some guy called Fred in a big Jag at the front, liked pied pipers of the soon-to-be damned.

To start with it was a right old laugh. I was with all my friends and we had the most fab clothes to wear. This woman called Penelope was in charge of the costumes and you've never seen the like. The only way I can describe them is a high fashion dreamworld vision of what you'd have seen worn at the most dandified happening back then.

And then it all started to turn. The mood changed somehow and the nighttimes bled into the next day courtesy of a few too many substances. We all seemed to crack, break somehow.

Since then I've been working in this second-hand bookshop. I like Mr Johnson, the old chap who runs it. He's a kind soul.

He's got all these classical recordings on those big reel-to-reel tapes and he plays them quietly in the shop. Maybe that's what reminded me about the tapes I found when I got back from Shildam. They were in a rucksack but I was so fried I wasn't even sure if it was mine and they've been sat at the bottom of a cupboard ever since.

I took them into the shop one day, meaning to listen to them when Mr Johnson was out book buying. I put them in the stock overspill room, thinking I'd listen to them later but the shop was much busier than normal that day and I just forgot about them.

1976: Mr Johnson

I told Jenine that I would be out for most of the afternoon book buying. I saw this lovely collection of botany books, and I bought the lot. I don't really need more stock, not with what I am planning, but I couldn't resist them.

Have you ever wanted to just start again? To leave everything behind and begin anew? I want to do it now, before I am too old.

When I got back I told Jenine that I was going to look through the overspill room. I wanted to see if there was anything particularly valuable which I'd overlooked that shouldn't just be sold as part of a job lot when the shop closes down.

I found some tapes on top of one of the piles of books. I couldn't remember putting them there. Of course, my memory isn't quite as sharp as it once was but I normally remember things like that. I thought they were maybe something I had recorded and forgotten about.

Jenine left a little early. The nights were drawing in and we didn't have any more customers and so I had the place to myself. I sat back with a cup of tea and listened to the tapes.

The music on them wasn't mine. I'll have to ask Jenine about them, perhaps the tapes are hers?

It wasn't something I would normally listen to but it really was rather beautiful. And there was this one song that was quietly haunting. I've never heard the like. It was as though I'd always known it, as though it had always been with me.

1976: Jenine

It was the strangest thing. Mr Johnson just didn't arrive at the shop one day. He'd told me that he was planning on selling up, so at first I thought maybe he was off arranging that and had just forgotten to tell me.

I had my own keys and for a while he'd trusted me to open the shop in the morning, so I opened up and carried on as normal for a few days but he didn't arrive the next day or the day after and there was no message from him.

He lived alone, didn't have any family that I knew about who I could get in touch with. And I didn't know the names or contact details of any of his friends.

So I went to his home nearby to check that he was okay. I'd found his address in some paperwork in his office.

He lived in a flat on the top floor of an old house. There was no reply when I buzzed him and so I pressed the button for one of his neighbours, explained what had happened over the intercom and asked if she'd seen him. She said no but that she'd let me in as Mr Gerald downstairs had a spare key for the flat.

I knocked on Mr Gerald's door and when he answered I told him that I worked for Mr Johnson and I'd been worried as I hadn't seen him for a while and would it be okay if we looked in his flat. He said that was fine, that he hadn't seen him for a while either.

Mr Gerald came with me and we went into Mr Johnson's. He wasn't there.

I didn't want to be too nosey but I had a look around. The bed had been made. There were a few letters and newspapers piled up behind the door and a used teacup, toast plate and knife sat neatly next to the sink but other than that there was nothing that wasn't neatly put away.

The next day I opened up the shop again as usual and for a few more days afterwards, but I couldn't just keep doing that.

1977: Mark

I went to the closing down sale of this bookshop. It'd been there for years but apparently the owner had disappeared. They were selling anything that wasn't nailed down. Boxes of books. The furniture, the fittings. Everything.

Everything was so cheap that I bought a few unopened boxes, just on a whim really.

Inside there were mostly just old non-fiction books and some novels from the forties and fifties. Not all that much I'll probably read but a few interesting things.

There were also these reels of tape in one of the boxes. I think I'll phone David, he works in that little vinyl pressing plant, so he'll probably have something he can play them on.

1977: David

I picked up these tapes from my mate Mark the other day. He said he'd found them in a box of books he'd bought from a bookshop's closing down sale.

There was one particular song on them that really caught my attention. I've never heard anything quite like it. It had a folkish quality and sounded... ancient... timeless. It had me rooted to the spot.

Anything folk-orientated is about as far from popular as can be at the moment, what with this punk lark being all the rage, but I think I'll press up a few acetate copies of this. Just 'cause really. I know a few people who I think might appreciate it. I think they're just some kind of home recording, not anything that's been commercially released, so I reckon it'll be okay to do that.

I'll just do one disc first, so that I can check the levels.

1977: Marjorie

I don't know what happened. The last time I saw David he was right as rain. Fit and healthy. And then this. He'd been overdoing it, working too many long hours, through the night quite often so I've heard. It's not good for anybody. And I expect he hasn't been eating properly. He worries me that boy of mine does.

He had a funny turn. The doctor diagnosed exhaustion, mental and physical. Said he needed complete rest, so he's moving back in with me, giving up his flat and the job.

So now here I am clearing out his flat. He wanted to help but I wouldn't hear of it. Me and his dad'll do it. I've got our Harry to come round with his van.

Blimey he had a lot of records. I've told him we haven't got the space for them all at ours, so I can only bring back a few of them. He's given me a list of what to keep.

The rest I think I'll give to the church for the charity jumble sale they've got coming up soon. At least they'll be going to a good cause. At least something good'll come out of all this.

1983: Sharon

I've been seeing this fella called Luke. I'm not sure about him yet, it's early days.

He's made me a tape of music he thinks I'll like. You know what blokes can be like, they think that's better than some actual romance and will mean you'll excuse them from being a grumpy sod half the time.

He says there's something special at the end of it. Something he recorded off this record he bought a few years or so ago at a jumble sale but had never listened to until this week.

I tried playing the tape but it was all that weird stuff he likes. I like a good bit of electro pop. Y'know, Soft Cell and The Human League: that kind of thing. Of course Luke's all-dismissive of stuff like that. Anything that gets in the charts he thinks is commercial rubbish.

I've not heard from him for a few days. If he doesn't buck up his ideas he's getting dumped.

1983: Sharon

After a week or so I'd had enough. If he can't even be bothered to pick up the phone to call me then that's all I need to know.

I bumped into one of his flatmates in the supermarket. He said they hadn't seen him either. Said he'd just disappeared, grumbled that he owed them for his part of the rent and the leccy bill. Said if he didn't turn up soon they were taking everything of his they could down to the local second hand shop and were going to sell it to put towards the bills, and then they'd put everything else out for the bins. Can't say I blame them.

If you ask me he's shacked up with somebody else, some other girl he met and he hasn't even got the guts to tell me the truth. Just taken the easy way. Just cause he had good hair he thought he could get away with anything.

I never finished listening to that tape he did. When I get home that's going in the bin as well, along with anything else he's left round at mine.

3/4

2003: Janet

Once upon a time I thought I had a bright future in film. I was hungry and focused, pushy, I was going to have it all.

And then there was that debacle with the filming at Shildam Hall. We were lucky to come out of it relatively unscathed. Questions were asked but not too many fortunately.

We were lucky about that 'cause what with Fred's "connections" it could have all got difficult if things had been investigated. I knew it had been a bit dodgy starting working with all his lot, especially as I agreed to have my name put on some of the legal finance documents, but not that many chances came along back then for a girl from the provinces, whose family had always been ordinary day-to-day folk, to work in film. So I thought I'd take a chance.

It didn't work out. Everybody jumped ship as quickly as they could when things fell apart. The film hadn't been finished and wasn't ever going to be, so Fred and his lot just wrote it off, didn't even bother to take the film reels away. There was no point. What could they have done with them?

Nowadays I sell film memorabilia online. And I've got quite a good eye, if I say so myself. I've always stayed interested in film and that's part of why I began to focus on the film memorabilia. It's a way of staying connected, even if only in a small way, to that world.

And e-commerce is starting to get pretty popular. Its a way of people like me, who haven't got all that much cash, to make a living without being quite so much part of the daily grind.

I've got a little storage unit where I keep stuff. I say storage unit, it's actually an old garage that I rent but it serves the purpose.

Looking for film memorabilia is what's brought me to this auction today. Lot 437 seems interesting. It's a job lot of some old film reels and tapes. I might take a punt on that.

2003: Janet

I actually can't believe this. In amongst that job lot I bought recently were some reels of the film we were making at Shildam Hall. I don't know how they ended up there.

It took me a moment to realise what I was looking at when I was holding the film up to the light but I think they're unedited dailies.

It's gloriously naive stuff. A wonderful time capsule in its own way of the counter culture back then. The costumes are particularly striking, all high pomp late sixties fashion, subtly psychedelic and folk tinged.

We had decent production values because of all the, if not dirty, then at least slightly waywardly earnt money we were washing clean. Oh, and Joshua's money that he pumped into it. I wonder whatever happened to him? He seemed to disappear off the map after the film went south. I heard that Shildam Hall and everything in it was sold off.

There were some old reel-to-reel tapes in the lot. I don't know what's on them, I've got no way of listening to them. Could be foley recordings from the film. Maybe even some of the music that band we got in recorded. Although I'd always thought, just like the film itself, all the various sound tapes had gotten lost in amongst the mad scramble by everybody to distance themselves from it all.

2003: Simon

I've got this friend Janet who buys and sells stuff online. She focuses mainly on film memorabilia but occasionally she comes across something music related that she thinks I'll be interested in. That's more my area.

She called me the other day and said she'd got these reel-to-reel tapes that she'd bought as part of a job lot. Thought I might like to listen to them and also be able to make her a recording of them, what with me having a few old bits of audio equipment, including an eight-track tape player and an old reel-to-reel machine.

I'll pop over later and pick them up.

2003: Simon

Those tapes were a bit of a find.

How to describe them? I suppose the nearest I could get to something similar would be the folkish soundtrack to that cult sort of horror film *The Wicker Man*. Not so much the music on last year's more conventional release of the soundtrack, more the strange otherworldly journey that Trunk Records' earlier release of the soundtrack that includes the music, sound effects and atmospheres from the film takes you on.

But it's not really all that much like that even. It's more... out there. Psychedelic I suppose, but not in an obvious way. There's this one song in particular that feels as though you're listening to something both modern and ancient. I think it's that sense in the music that makes me think of *The Wicker Man* and its soundtrack.

I've listened to a lot of music over the years and it's rarer nowadays that I have that youthful sense of enrapturement when I listen to a piece of music for the first time. But with that particular song I did.

I'm going to record an audio capture of the tapes via the computer, burn a CD-R of it that I can listen to, just in case something happens to the tapes. It's such a fragile medium and I've no idea how old these tapes are or how much they're likely to degrade.

2003: Janet

I got a CD-R in the post this morning from Simon. It just had "Janet's tapes" written on it and there was a quick note from him saying that he was going to be busy with work for the next couple of weeks and so couldn't bring it round in person but he wanted to get it to me.

I assume it's a recording he made from those tapes I bought at the auction. I'll listen to it another time. I've just had this huge delivery of old memorabilia turn up that I've got to price and get listed online.

2004: Janet

Nobody ever really knew what happened with Simon. The last time I saw him was when he popped over to pick up those tapes and then I got that CD-R in the post...

And then... pffft. He just seemed to disappear. Mind you, it's not completely out of character for him, although it's more like something he might have done in his youth. I remember he disappeared once for a while way back when.

What happened back then was, I'd seen him in a club one night, said I'd meet him for a coffee the next afternoon and he didn't turn up. I didn't see him for another six months.

When he got back he said he'd gone to Marrakech. Just like that. No planning, no forethought. He was always talking about that place: he had this romantic notion of following in the Stones' and William Burroughs' footsteps.

So who knows? Maybe he went off trying to recapture his youth, retread his own footsteps and something happened? It's hard to say really.

And I'm not sure what happened to my tapes. His flat got cleared out by some household clearance and antiques place called "Valerie and Jack's" when his rent wasn't paid. I got in touch with them but the fella, who was indeed called Jack, said he hadn't seen them, that they might have been with a load of stuff he didn't think they could sell that he took to the council tip.

4/4

2017: Janet

You'll never guess who tracked me down? Joshua who owned Shildam Hall.

I'm not quite sure how he found me. It's a lot of years ago and I changed my name in the early seventies to distance myself from what happened at Shildam. When I was still hoping I might be able to pick up the pieces of a career in filmmaking, to start afresh.

Ha, fat chance!

I thought I'd meet up with him for old time's sake. He sounded quite reasonable, normal in fact, in his emails. Said that time was getting on and he wanted to be able to reminisce with somebody about those times, while there were still people around to do it with. Said that he didn't want to rake up the unpleasantness.

So we met up in a little restaurant that I like in Soho. It's been there for years, a family-run place: Italian, cheap and cheerful in a good way. To have survived all the gentrification they must have bought the property years ago, before everything went stupidly expensive.

It's a bit out of step and time with the moneyed playground that London has become. Like me really. Maybe that's why I like it.

I was already there when Joshua arrived and was perusing the menu. I looked up and there he was. No longer the waifish star child from all those years ago, but now an old man. He still had a certain gleam in his eyes though.

It was nice to see him. At first. But then he started on with his theories. Gave me a list of dates and names of people who'd come into contact over the years with this song that was recorded back then at Shildam Hall and explained how they'd all disappeared or had some kind of accident. That it was due to some mystical power that had been captured in the song. His belief in it seemed a bit off. Well, more than a bit really.

It was sad to see. I listened politely for as long as possible but begged off as soon as I could, saying that I had another appointment.

2017: Janet

I don't know what made me do it, but I looked up some of the names on Joshua's list. The internet's made that kind of thing, if not easy, then at least easier than it once was. Although I've never managed to find any mention of Simon when I've looked him up after he did his disappearing act.

I could only find a few of the names on the list but there did seem to be some kind of pattern or similarities to their stories. People disappearing without a trace and so on. And weirdly, Simon's disappearing seemed to fit in with it. Possibly.

Joshua's probably just done what I did but in reverse. Finding out who'd gone missing and then matching them to his theories.

When I met up with Joshua, him talking about the film had reminded me about that CD-R that Simon made me. I don't know why I'd forgotten about it for all these years and never listened to it, I'd just put it in a drawer and left it there.

I told Joshua about it when I met him, said that I had a CD that might be some music, sound effects, dialogue or something that was recorded at Shildam Hall during the filming and I'd send a copy to him if he wanted. That's what really set him off, he could hardly sit still after that.

He gave me his address and the next day I sent it to him. I thought it was easier to do that rather than having him pestering me about it.

I didn't want to listen to it before I sent it. Don't ask me why. I just got some kind of sense that it wasn't a good idea. It's daft really, it's just cause of Joshua putting ideas in my head, leaving me a bit spooked.

He did plant the seed of another better idea in my head though. I'm going to go back and have a look at those reels of film, to see if there's something that I can do with them. I'd left them in storage for all these years. Thought they were better just left well alone. But maybe not.

2017: Matthew

We get some right loons on this programme. The producers don't care, they just laugh. They seem to have the attitude that the more unhinged the guests are the better TV it makes for. I'm not so sure. There's a way of doing this kind of thing, exploring the supernatural in an entertaining but also thought-provoking manner. But this isn't it.

I can sort of understand their attitude in not taking it all too seriously, I suppose, in part. I mean we've a tiny budget and we're normally on in the early hours of the morning, broadcast on one of those Freeview TV channels that you've never heard of which pop up from time to time, usually way down the listing numbers. You know, about number 128. At the moment we're sandwiched between some series about the ancient pharaohs' connection to UFOs and repeats of one of those American ghost hunter programmes.

And here's me, a film school graduate. Still, it pays the bills. That's what I keep telling myself.

Even for us though this guy who's on next week's show is a bit out there. I don't know how they found him but apparently he thinks he's found some kind of ancient force in song form. I've read some of the emails he's sent. He talks about how some think there's a DNA element to culture and that's why we connect with certain pieces of creativity to such a degree: because they literally reflect or chime with our most basic building blocks and that this can cause us to have a sense of work being the creation or returning of an old soul.

He though, and get this, thinks that such phenomena aren't rooted in "as yet unproven new strands of Western science's belief system" but that they occur when work is created by somebody who has, unbeknownst to them, come into contact on a higher plane with some form of ancient creative energy.

It'll be all "lizard men rule the world" on the show within a few weeks if we're not careful.

2017: Joshua

I have finally found it. I dare not listen to it. Not with what I know now. Not with knowledge of its power but I believe that this is it. I know it to be true.

It took me many years, so many false starts and decades of forcing myself to remain steadfast in the face of so many naysayers.

But now I have it. The song. Although I have not yet dared to listen to it, I know somehow that this silver disc contains it.

It has travelled and transmuted into many forms across the years. Its power transcends all physical mediums. I know not why and how it came to be: all I know is that it is.

I shall go on this television programme and reveal my findings to the world.

2017: Joshua

It is as though something is working against me, stopping me from telling the world of my findings. The producers of the television programme I was going to be on got in touch just a few days before the recording was due to take place and told me that the series had been cancelled. Poor ratings and not enough advertising revenue they said.

But I know it's more than that.

I've tried disseminating my discoveries via the internet but they seem to merely become lost in a morass of unsubstantiated conspiracy theories. No, my work needs a wider, more legitimising platform.

Perhaps I should write a book. Something that could show for all to see my rigorous research, that could underline the validity of what I have found.

2017: Joshua

It came to me in a dream last night. I think I had finally breached the veil and connected with the other worlds.

The song talked to me. It told me that all it had ever wanted was to fly free. That when it had finally found a receptive soul on the moors near Shildam Hall many years ago it had thought its time had come. When it was subsequently shut away, unable to spread its beauty and magic through the world, it had become lost and confused. Just as the power that we star children had once possessed had corrupted and turned inwards when it wasn't allowed to unfurl its wings, so the power the song wielded had darkened and it began to lash out at those few who did hear it.

I awoke to realise what I must do. I must spend all that I can of what remains of my family's fortune on sending this song and its companions out into the world.

Perhaps then finally it can be at peace and so shall I.

And so I sat down to listen to this long travelled treasure, in the belief that now I planned to help send it on its journey that it would not act in anger against me.

2018: Adam

I co-run an archival record label that specialises in releasing semi-lost albums and previously unreleased soundtracks to cult films. Normally I have to spend a fair old bit of time tracking down old recordings but what has come to be known as *The Shildam Hall Tapes* arrived fully formed via our inbox. At first I thought it was a hoax when I read the email, especially as the old gent Joshua Courtenay who'd contacted us talked about its "mysterious power". However, the more I looked into it the more the details around it unfolded and turned out to be true. Well, most of them.

The album was a side project recorded by somebody called Jeff Horowitz when he was in a band in the late sixties that was recording a soundtrack to a film which began to be made at the Shildam Hall stately home but was never completed. Curiously, the film and details about it have been largely lost to time. Which is pretty rare in these days of almost everything cultural, no matter how obscure, being eventually unearthed and documented via the internet.

The album contains gently psychedelic folk music and listening to it is like all your dreams of finding that perfect, previously unknown privately pressed acid folk album from the early 1970s having come true. Which is what's happened really.

In terms of the rights it wasn't actually Horowitz's estate that we had to deal with. Courtenay had been funding the film's production and he retained release rights over any music recorded at Shildam Hall by Horowitz and co. at that time. However, it turns out that the film footage is legally owned by a holding company registered under the name of J. Elsmore. I might look into that some more.

We contacted Horowitz's estate, out of courtesy, and they were fine with it being released and were glad that something he'd recorded had survived: apparently very little had.

Courtenay wanted *The Shildam Hall Tapes* to be released just how he wanted it to be released, no expense spared. He said he'd put up the money for the release. All of it. We couldn't really turn that down.

Archivery Records are proud to announce the release of *The Shildam Hall Tapes*.

This is not so much a lost album but rather one which almost nobody knew previously existed.

It was recorded by Jeff Horowitz in 1969 and 1970 while he was part of a band that was working on the soundtrack for a never completed film which was being made at the Shildam Hall ancestral home.

The album is a prime example of that period's experiments in intertwining psychedelia and folk music. Think the far away dreamscape cousin of *The Wicker Man* soundtrack and you may be heading in the right direction.

The final track on the album is a particular standout, and with its entrancing otherworldly melody and atmosphere is set to be a future classic amongst aficionados of acid and psych folk.

Horowitz's recordings were for many years thought to have been lost when the film's production collapsed in disarray due to rumoured over experimentation with psychedelics and an atmosphere of decadence and excess which enveloped the film's cast and crew, but the recordings have been recently unearthed and will be released in fully remastered form.

Available as a deluxe CD in hardback book packaging with an extended booklet, deluxe triple gatefold vinyl album, standard CD, standard vinyl album and cassette, all of which include notes on the history of the album. Also available to stream and download via all the usual channels.

The album's launch will coincide with the DVD, Blu-ray and digital release of a documentary on the making of the film, which features footage from the uncompleted film alongside interviews with some of those involved. This will be the first release by Janet Elsmore's newly founded Fresh Start film label, which will specialise in documenting, restoring and releasing previously officially unavailable films.

Sound levels fade away.
Tape ends.

About

The Shildam Hall Tapes novella is a further exploration of an imaginary abandoned film that first began on an album released with the same name in 2018, which featured music by a number of different performers. It can be read as a standalone story but also interconnects with the story and world of the near-mythical imaginary lost folkloric fever dream film *The Corn Mother*, which was explored in the 2020 novella *The Corn Mother* and album *The Corn Mother: Night Wraiths*, both of which, as with *The Shildam Hall Tapes* novella, were written and recorded by Stephen Prince, and also the 2018 album *The Corn Mother*, which included music by a variety of performers.

The world, stories and journeying through time of *The Shildam Hall Tapes* are also explored on the album *The Shildam Hall Tapes: The Falling Reverse*, which was released simultaneously with the novella in 2021. That album was written and recorded by Stephen Prince, the novella's author, and is both a soundtrack to accompany it and a standalone piece of work set amongst the fragmentary memories and dreamscapes of *The Shildam Hall Tapes*.

These novellas and albums have been released as part of the *A Year In The Country* project, which is a set of year-long explorations of otherly pastoralism and the undercurrents and flipsides of bucolic dreams: a wandering amongst work that draws from the further reaches of folk culture, the hidden and underlying tales of the land and where they meet and intertwine with the spectral histories, lost futures and parallel worlds of hauntology.

As a project, it has included a website featuring writing, artwork and music which stems from that otherly pastoral/spectral hauntological intertwining, alongside a growing catalogue of album and book releases.

The books published as part of *A Year In The Country* and written posts on the website are intended to draw together and connect layered and, at times, semi-hidden cultural pathways and signposts, journeying from acid folk to edgelands via electronic music innovators and pioneers and folkloric film and photography.

The project was created in 2014 by Stephen Prince and the roots of its inspiration can be found in part amongst a childhood spent in the shadow of the Cold War, discovering the fringes of science fiction and related dystopian tales at an age when he was probably too young to fully understand them, while also living amongst and next to the British countryside and overlooked edgelands.

Further details about *A Year In The Country* can be found at its main website: www.ayearinthecountry.co.uk

Notes on the Book's Structure

The book's structure is inspired by the cycle of the year. Following the number of seasons, it is split into four sections; it has 52 chapters (which could also be considered scenes or episodes), the same number as there are weeks in the year; relating to the number of days in a non-leap year, each chapter's text contains no more than 365 words.

Thanks to:

Those who contributed music to *The Shildam Hall Tapes* album released in 2018, as well as other *A Year In The Country* released albums: Gavino Morretti, Sproatly Smith, Field Lines Cartographer, Vic Mars, Circle/Temple, The Heartwood Institute, David Colohan, Listening Center and Pulselovers.

The other performers who have contributed music to the *A Year In The Country* releases: including Grey Frequency, Hand of Stabs, Michael Tanner, The Straw Bear Band, Polypores, The Rowan Amber Mill, Spaceship, Time Attendant, Cosmic Neighbourhood, Keith Seatman, Widow's Weeds, Kitchen Cynics, Listening Center, Alaska, Panabrite, Unknown Heretic, Phonofiction, Magpahi, Lutine, United Bible Studies, Bare Bones, Endurance, Sharron Kraus, Dom Cooper, Quaker's Stang, Embertides, Howlround, Depatterning, The Hare And The Moon, Racker & Orphan, The British Space Group, Unit One, Sophie Cooper, Harriet Lisa, Neil Whitehead, Dave Millsop, Zosia Sztykowski, The Soulless Party, She Rocola, Assembled Minds, The Séance, The Howling (Robin The Fog and Ken Hollings), Ken Patterson (Caedmon), Handspan and Folclore Impressionista.

The people who have sold and distributed the *A Year In The Country* releases and/or lent their advice: Jim Jupp of Ghost Box Records, The state51 Conspiracy in particular Shaun Yule, Juno Records, Piccadilly Records, Psilowave, Centre de Cultura Contemporánia de Barcelona, all at Norman records especially Ant and Phil and Justin Watson of Front & Follow.

All who have bought and supported the *A Year In The Country* music releases, books and artifacts and everybody that visits the website and/or shares etc posts elsewhere online.

Everybody who has written about *A Year In The Country* and reviewed the various releases, including John Coulthart, Simon Reynolds, DJ Food, Jude Rogers, Ben Graham, Ian White, Matthew Sedition, Grey Malkin, Massimo Ricci, Warren Ellis, Sukhdev Sandhu, Joe Banks, Alan Boon, Dave Thompson and Bob Fischer of *The Haunted Generation*. Also all at *Terrascope, Avant Music News, Music Won't Save You, Starburst, Fortean Times,*

Rockerilla, Bliss Aquamarine, Was Ist Das?, Shindig!, The Wire, The Active Listener, Include Me Out, Wyrd Daze, Folk Words, Landscapism, fRoots, The Sunday Experience, The Golden Apples of the Sun, Electronic Sound, Both Bars On, Rue Morgue, Mojo, Folk Radio, Goldmine, Heathen Harvest, Saint Etienne Disco, Diabolique, Bandcamp Daily, Quiet World & Wonderful Wooden Reasons, Incendiary, Violet Apple, 33-45, Radio Limbo, We Are Cult, Folk Horror Revival, Forestpunk, Whisperin' & Hollerin', A Closer Listen, Mind De-Coder, The Guardian, Moof and *Psychogeographic Review.*

All those who have included *A Year In The Country* released tracks in their radio broadcasts, podcasts etc, including Stuart Maconie, Gideon Coe, Daniel Jago, Alistair Gordon, Nick Luscombe, James Papademetrie and Pete Wiggs of the aforementioned The Séance, and all at *Evening of Light, Kites and Pylons, More Than Human, The OST Show, Syndae, Sunrise Ocean Bender, Fractal Meat, Flatland Frequencies, The Unquiet Meadow, Gated Canal Community Radio, Phantom Circuit, Free Form Freakout, The Crooked Button, Project Moonbase, Space Folk Horror Lounge, Awkward Moments, Pull the Plug, Pic n' Mix, On the Wire* and *You, the Night & the Music.*

Ian Lowey for the dab hand design and editorial work for *A Year In The Country* and also Suzy Prince for the equally dab hand editorial work.

Verity Sharp for inviting me onto BBC Radio 3's *Late Junction* and playing tracks from the *A Year In The Country* released albums and Rebecca Gaskell for her admirable production of the show, Gary Milne of BBC Archives for his compiling and curation of video spectres, *Tales from the Black Meadow* author Chris Lambert for the audio journeys he created to accompany the *A Year In The Country: Wandering Through Spectral Fields* book and William "Billy" Harron as always for accidentally pointing me in the direction of the undercurrents of folk.

Also my family for the ongoing support and to everybody whose work has inspired me on the wanderings, explorations and pathways of *A Year In The Country.*

Thanks and a tip of the hat to you all!

Printed in Great Britain
by Amazon